MYTHICAL CREATURES

WHAT CREATURES
LURK INSIDE?
--
BEWARE!
--
READ ON
IF YOU DARE...

Dear Reader

Are you ready to start a journey that will take you back into the swirling mists of ancient times? You will need a shield to protect yourself from the fangs and blazing heat of fire-breathing dragons, and a sword to ward off monstrous beasts such as the dreadful snake-like Hydra, with its nine hissing heads.

You will cross the great continents of the world, from the ice-bound north to the heat-struck landscapes of Africa and Asia. But wherever you go, keep your eyes and wits about you! Beware of the dreaded Harpies, who fly down from the skies, screeching and ready to attack with their filthy claws. Look out for the Cyclopes, the one-eyed giants who will eat you alive if you don't escape their huge hands.

And don't think you will be safer travelling by sea. For there, beneath the waves, lurks Charybdis, the monster that sucks down ships to their destruction, as well as the fearsome Kraken, as big as an island!

But you will witness marvels of beauty too. If you see a flash of light in the sky, it may be the wondrous phoenix with its glittering wings. And if you travel through forests, you might glimpse the shy, snow-white unicorn darting behind a bush.

Travel light, with open eyes and an open heart, and you will find a world you never suspected – a world of the past that still lurks in the shadows of the present.

Go now, and take your courage with you!

MYTHICAL CREATURES

as told by

JAMES HARPUR

and

illustrated by

STUART MARTIN

CARLTON
BOOKS

GIANTS

Huge, lumbering creatures, giants are one of the world's most distinctive monsters.

Ancient Greek tales describe a race of one-eyed, man-eating giants known as the Cyclopes, while Irish myths tell of the deadly one-eyed giant named Balor. In Scandinavia, evil giants known as trolls leave their cave dwellings at night to prey on human flesh.

The Mighty Cyclops

According to the epic poem the *Odyssey*, the Greek hero Odysseus and his men were returning home from the Trojan war when they landed near the island of the Cyclopes. They came across a huge cave where they found food and drink. A Cyclops – a one-eyed giant – thundered into the cave, closing the entrance with an enormous stone. He snatched up two of the Greeks and ate them for his supper. The next day, the Cyclops ate two more sailors for breakfast before leaving the cave with his sheep flocks – blocking up the entrance with the stone. Odysseus and his men sharpened the giant's pole-like club, which he had left in the cave. When the Cyclops returned, the giant drank a bowl of red wine, then asked Odysseus his name. The hero told him that it was "Nobody". The giant soon got drunk with wine, then fell asleep.

& TROLLS

Man-eating Trolls

Scandinavian trolls are ugly giants that dwell in caves. They prefer mountainous country, and hunt by night. Beware, for they are very fond of human flesh! However, you should be safe in daylight hours, for exposure to sunlight is said to turn these creatures to stone.

"The Cyclops stuffed his vast stomach with human flesh and drank some milk. He then lay down inside his cave and stretched himself out among his sheep."

– Greek writer Homer

BLINDING THE MONSTER

Seizing their chance, Odysseus and his men grabbed the wooden stake and drove it into the giant's eye. He roared in agony, crying out for help from his fellow Cyclopes, who lived nearby. When these giants asked their friend who was hurting him, he cried out "Nobody!", and they thought he was playing the fool.

Eventually, the Greeks escaped from the cave by clinging to the undersides of the giant's sheep as they were let out to graze. The Cyclops felt the backs of his flock but could not see the sailors beneath the sheep. As soon as they were clear of the cave, the Greeks ran back to their ship.

The Deadly Balor

In Irish legend there was once a battle between a supernatural people named the Tuatha Dé Danann and the Fomorians. A giant named Balor was the Fomorians' champion: this monster's single eye gave off a poisonous beam that could kill people instantly!

At the climax of the battle, Balor commanded four men to pull up his huge eyelid. But, as the lid was lifted up, the Tuatha Dé Danann hero Lugh let loose a slingstone at the deadly eye. The stone smashed the eye out of the back of Balor's head. With their hero dead, the Fomorians lost heart and were driven back to the sea.

HALF HUMAN, HALF BEAST!

CREATURES THAT COMBINE THE PHYSICAL FEATURES OF HUMAN BEINGS WITH THOSE OF ANIMALS OFTEN APPEAR IN MYTHS AND LEGENDS.

One of the most notorious of these beasts was the dreaded Minotaur – a bull-headed monster that was kept in a maze built by King Minos of Crete. Other hybrids include the half-human, half-horse centaurs, and satyrs, whose human upper bodies sit on the legs of a horse or a goat.

Centaurs at the Wedding Feast

Centaurs have the torsos of men and the bodies and four legs of a horse. They live in mountain regions, especially the wilds of Thessaly in northern Greece. Centaurs hunt animals and are prone to quarrelling with their neighbours. One famous fight took place at the wedding feast of Peirithous, the king of a wild tribe known as the Lapiths. Peirithous was marrying Hippodamia and had invited the centaurs to the banquet. During the feast, the centaurs got drunk and became filled with desire for all the women present, including Hippodamia herself! Swords slashed and tables were overturned, but the Lapiths drove the centaurs out of the palace.

Party Animals!

The greatest party-goers in myths are satyrs. Their hair is bristly and they have round, turned-up noses, animal ears (and sometimes horns), and the legs of a horse or a goat. Satyrs love drinking and going to feasts, dressed in animal skins. They are often found dancing with (or chasing!) nymphs, and they like to liven things up with their music.

Honoured in the Stars

The wisest of all the centaurs was Chiron, tutor to a number of Greek heroes. He was wounded accidentally by a poisoned arrow, but was unable to die because he was immortal. Eventually Zeus, king of the gods, allowed Chiron to die and honoured him with a place in the sky as the constellation Centaurus (some say Sagittarius).

The Bull-Man Minotaur

The Minotaur had the head of bull and the torso and legs of a human being. The offspring of Pasiphäe, King Minos's wife, and a bull, the Minotaur was a ferocious creature that gorged itself on human flesh. Minos kept the beast shut up at the centre of a complex maze at his palace, where its dreadful bellowing echoed through the passageways.

Every nine years, Minos ordered seven young men and seven maidens from Athens to be abandoned in the maze as a sacrifice to the Minotaur. The Athenian hero Theseus decided he would end this slaughter, and kill the Minotaur. Handsome and dashing, he soon caught the eye of Minos's daughter, Princess Ariadne, who decided to help Theseus fulfil his mission.

ARIADNE'S THREAD

The princess gave Theseus a thread to help him retrace his steps out of the labyrinth. He attached the thread to the entrance of the maze and began to advance towards the centre. Soon the blood-curdling roars of the Minotaur reached his ears but Theseus continued bravely on. After many false turns, he eventually reached the monster and managed to kill it with his bare hands! He then followed the thread all the way out of the maze and escaped from the island.

DRAGONS OF THE ORIENT

IN MANY PARTS OF THE WORLD, THE DRAGON IS A FEARED MONSTER, BREATHING FIRE AND TERRORIZING VILLAGES. BUT IN CHINA AND OTHER PARTS OF THE EAST THIS HAS NOT ALWAYS BEEN THE CASE.

In China, dragons are believed to be bringers of good luck and wealth. Temples and shrines are built in their honour. The Japanese also have dragons, most of them living in watery dwellings, such as seas and lakes. One of these was O-gon-cho, a dragon who transformed itself every 50 years into a golden bird.

The Dragon's Body

Most Chinese dragons are associated with water, clouds, rivers and other natural features, and the dragon is also held to be the ancestor of the Chinese emperors. A Chinese dragon's body is long and has the scales of a carp, while its head resembles that of a horse or camel. It has deer-like horns and the eyes of demons. It does not usually have wings, but instead can rise to the sky with the help of a hump below its horns, which acts as a sort of air-propulsion device. Its legs are short and its feet generally have four dangerous claws (imperial dragons have five). Japanese dragons have only three claws on each of their four feet.

DRAGONS – AND MORE DRAGONS!

Chinese dragons are divided into different groups. There are celestial dragons, who guard the palaces of the gods and pull their chariots; spiritual or divine dragons, who make the rain fall and control the winds; dragons of hidden treasures, who guard the wealth or treasures of the earth; underground dragons, associated with rivers; winged dragons, who can fly through the sky; and yellow dragons, renowned for their knowledge.

The Year of the Dragon

The Chinese calendar is based on the cycles of the moon. It has a 12-year cycle, during which each year is associated with a traditional animal, such as the Rat or Tiger. Each animal is associated with a set of personality traits, and these are thought to influence those who are born in a particular year. For example, people born during the year of the Rat are said to be imaginative, while Snake types are considered wise.

The year of the Dragon will next occur in 2012. Dragon types have the dragon-like ability to soar to the skies with their ambitious ideas, and they are confident and brave. At times they can be hot-headed and insensitive, but on the whole they are considered generous and attractive, enjoying life to the full and providing leadership to others.

The Golden Dragon Bird

According to Japanese tradition, the people of the city of Kyoto were once menaced by a huge white dragon. It lived nearby in the murky darkness of a lake. Sometimes it rose to the surface when the weather was fine, but it did not stay for long, soon sinking back to the lake's depths.

Every 50 years, however, the dragon changed its shape and became a giant bird with wings of glowing yellow feathers. The Japanese called it the Golden Bird, or O-gon-cho. After its transformation, it would rise up into the sky uttering a terrible wolf-like howl. When they heard this noise, the people all around believed that some natural disaster would befall the land, such as drought, famine or pestilence.

DRAGONS OF THE WEST

IN THE LEGENDS OF THE WEST, DRAGONS ARE ALMOST ALWAYS MONSTROUS BEASTS, BREATHING FIRE OR POISONOUS FUMES. THEY HAVE SCALY BODIES AND WINGS, RAZOR-SHARP CLAWS AND FEROCIOUS FANGS.

Dragon stories have been told for thousands of years. In the Bible's Book of Revelation, a seven-headed dragon with ten horns was defeated by the archangel Michael. Other famous dragon stories involve the Christian saint George and the Greek hero Jason.

St George and the Dragon

The town of Silene in Libya was under constant attack by a fearsome dragon, which lived in a nearby swamp. This terrifying beast would emerge from the water, flapping its great wings and belching poisonous fumes from its nostrils as it pounced on any living thing. The people of Silene fed the dragon with two sheep every day, but the dragon continued to cause havoc. It was decided to present the beast with a human sacrifice; the Silenians drew lots, and the victim turned out to be none other than the king of Silene's young daughter!

THE BEAST DESTROYED

The princess was left at the swamp to meet her fate. By a stroke of luck, St George, the brave patron saint of England and Portugal, was riding past. When the snarling dragon appeared, it ran at St George, who managed to protect himself with his shield. George aimed his spear at a spot under the dragon's wing where he could see there were no protective scales, and plunged it deep into the creature's flesh. With a terrible roar of pain, the mighty beast fell to the ground. St George then led the creature back to Silene, where he cut off its head.

The Dragon of the Golden Fleece

The young Greek hero Jason was determined to regain the throne of Iolcus, a city in northern Greece, where his father had been overthrown by his brother Pelias. Pelias told Jason that he would hand the throne to him if Jason could obtain the Golden Fleece – the pelt of a golden ram kept as a treasure by King Aeëtes of Colchis (by the Black Sea). The fleece was guarded by a terrible dragon that never slept, and Pelias was sure that Jason would never return!

Jason assembled a group of heroes to help him. They sailed off in a ship called the *Argo* and, after many adventures, they arrived at Colchis. There, King Aeëtes agreed to let Jason attempt to take the fleece on condition that he performed a dangerous task that included yoking two fire-breathing bulls and ploughing a field with them. The king's daughter, a sorceress named Medea, had fallen in love with Jason, and gave him a magic potion that helped the hero to carry out this challenge successfully.

"The dragon with his keen sleepless eyes saw them coming, and stretched out his long neck and gave a terrifying hiss ..."

– Apollonius of Rhodes describing
the dragon guarding
the Golden Fleece

PUTTING THE DRAGON TO SLEEP

Next, accompanied by Medea, Jason set off to fetch the Golden Fleece, which hung from the branch of an oak tree in a sacred grove. As he approached the tree, Jason could see the serpent-like dragon wrapped around it. The beast's terrifying eyes were wide open, and its spine-chilling hiss echoed around the groves and riverbanks.

Instead of attacking the dragon with his sword, Jason took Medea's advice and relied on a magic sleeping potion that she managed to sprinkle and smear over the creature. Soon the dragon fell into a deep sleep, and Jason was able to snatch the fleece from the tree before making his way back to the *Argo*.

HORRIFYING HYBRIDS

Some of the most nightmarish creatures of myth are hybrids — those made up of parts of different animals. Monsters such as the Greek Chimera and Sphinx terrified those who encountered them.

I n Egypt, too, hybrid creatures were widely known — for example, the chilling crocodile-headed demon Ammut who lived in the underworld. She had the body of a leopard and the backside of a hippopotamus, and sat at the judgement of the dead, ready to devour the souls of the unworthy.

The Fire-Breathing Chimera

The Chimera's main body and head were those of a lion, but a goat's head poked up from its back, and a snake writhed where its tail should have been. The fire-breathing beast terrorized Lycia (in western Turkey). The king of Lycia, Iobates, challenged the young hero Bellerophon to kill the Chimera. With the help of a golden bridle given to him by the goddess Athene, Bellerophon was able to capture a winged horse named Pegasus to assist him. Together they soared high into the air, scanning the land. Eventually they saw the hideous Chimera in the distance, destroying bushes and trees with its breath.

THE MONSTER IS KILLED

Bellerophon and Pegasus swept down towards the beast but the Chimera saw them coming. Pegasus managed to dodge its fiery breath, and Bellerophon fired arrows at the monster. One hit the Chimera's side; another entered its mouth. The creature crumpled dead to the ground, its fire forever extinguished.

Ammut: Devourer of Hearts

In Egyptian myth, the underworld demon Ammut was terrible to behold. Her head was that of a crocodile, while her body took the form of a lion at the front, and of a hippopotamus at the back. These animals were ones the Egyptians most feared in everyday life — a creature made up of all three of them was horrific!

Known as the Devourer, Ammut took part in the underworld judgement of the dead, a ceremony presided over by the dog-headed god Anubis. The heart of a dead person was put in a jar and placed in one of two scales. The feather of Ma'at (the goddess of Truth and Justice) was placed in the other one. If the heart did not balance the feather, it was deemed to be sinful and was thrown to Ammut, who ate it. If the heart passed the test, the mortal was allowed to progress farther on his or her journey through the underworld.

The Theban Sphinx

In ancient Greece, the people of Thebes were menaced by a terrible creature known as the Sphinx. She lived on a mountain near the city, and bore a woman's face and chest, merged with a lion's body. In addition, she had eagles' wings and a serpent's tail.

The Sphinx terrorized the Thebans by constantly challenging them to answer a riddle. If they were unable to do so correctly, she strangled them. The citizens became so desperate to rid themselves of this monster that their king, Creon, offered his throne to anyone who could solve the puzzle!

The challenge was accepted by a man named Oedipus. Approaching the Sphinx, he calmly listened to her question and was able to answer correctly. Enraged that her power had been broken, the Sphinx ended her life by throwing herself off the mountain. Oedipus was rewarded for freeing the Thebans from the curse by being made king.

CAN YOU SOLVE THE RIDDLE OF THE SPHINX?

What has four legs in the morning, two legs in the afternoon and three legs in the evening?

See right of the page for the answer.

"It was a lion in front, a snake behind, and a goat in the middle, and it belched out a terrible flame of dazzling fire."

– Greek writer Homer describing the Chimera

RIDDLE ANSWER

The answer is Man. For it is man who walks on all fours when he is a baby, on two legs when he is grown up, and with two legs and a stick, when he is elderly.

DEADLY SERPENTS

SNAKES AND SERPENTS CAN BE FOUND IN MYTHS ALL OVER THE WORLD. SOMETIMES THEY ARE SEEN AS EVIL, DANGEROUS CREATURES. BUT BECAUSE THEY CAN SHED THEIR SKINS AND ARE ASSOCIATED WITH THE EARTH, SNAKES ALSO SYMBOLIZE LIFE, RENEWAL AND ENERGY.

The dark side of snakes can be seen in the Bible, where it is the serpent who tempts Eve to eat the fruit of the Tree of Knowledge. Also, the Christian saint Patrick is said to have banished all the snakes from Ireland. And in Greek myth, the god Apollo killed the giant Python who guarded the holy shrine of Delphi. On the other hand, the Greek god of healing, Aesculapius, carried a rod with a snake entwined round it – a symbol of life still used today.

The Midgard Serpent

In Norse myth, there was a giant serpent named Jormungand. It was so large that it encircled the Earth. It could crush its victims with its massive coils and kill with its deadly venom. Odin, the father of the gods, decided to get rid of Jormungand by throwing the serpent into the sea.

THOR'S FISHING TRIP

One of the best-known stories involving Jormungand was its encounter with the god of thunder Thor. Hymir, who was a giant, and Thor decided to go out fishing on the ocean. They soon came to a spot where Hymir was used to catching lots of fish. However, Thor was keen to go out farther, and continued to row. Hymir started to get worried: they had gone out so far that they were in danger of being attacked by the serpent!

However, Thor took no notice of his companion. When he eventually stopped rowing, far out in the ocean, Thor prepared his fishing line. He had brought a huge ox's head as bait, and he skewered it on a large hook. He then threw the line overboard, and settled down to wait.

LANDING THE MONSTER

The Midgard Serpent soon struck, biting the bait and getting the hook stuck in its mouth. It tugged hard at the line against the boat. Thor rose to the challenge of this tug-of-war. But the serpent fought on, spitting out venom. As Thor grabbed his hammer to strike the beast, the terrified Hymir lost his nerve and cut Thor's line. Thor was furious, but there was nothing he could do. The evil serpent slithered away, returning to its watery home.

The Hydra

Another terrifying serpent-like monster was the Hydra, who lived in the swamp of Lerna near the city of Argos in southern Greece. The Hydra's body was that of a huge, thick serpent, on top of which writhed nine snarling heads (some stories say it had up to a hundred!). One of these heads could not be killed, and if any of the other eight were cut off, two heads sprang up to replace it. The Hydra's poison could kill any living creature. For years it preyed upon people and cattle foolish enough to stray near its watery hide-out. But then came its encounter with the Greek hero Heracles.

"Heracles found the Hydra on a ridge beside the springs of Amymone where it nested. By throwing flaming spears at it he forced it to come down, and as it did he was able to grab it."

– Greek writer Apollodorus

Heracles and the Hydra

Famed for his great strength and daring, Heracles was once ordered to carry out 12 highly dangerous tasks. The second of these was to kill the Hydra. Heracles set out in his chariot to the swamp of Lerna where he spotted the serpent perched on a ridge beside a spring. He threw flaming spears at the Hydra, forcing it to leave its position. As the monster slithered towards him, Heracles grabbed it and struck off one of its heads with his club. To his horror, two heads immediately sprang up in its place. To make matters worse, a giant crab attacked the hero, biting him on the foot. Heracles was able to kill the crab and retreat to hatch another plan of attack, this time enlisting the help of his friend, Iolaus.

The Death of a Monster

Running to a nearby wood, Iolaus gathered pieces of wood and set these on fire. The two men then attacked the Hydra with a pincer-assault. Heracles cut off one of the beast's heads, and Iolaus immediately thrust a burning stick onto the oozing stump to stop the replacement head from sprouting. Finally, Heracles was left with only the immortal head. This he chopped off, then quickly buried it by the roadside. To make sure it could not re-emerge, he placed a huge boulder on top. He then dipped his arrows into the poison of the monster's corpse. These would make lethal weapons against future enemies!

The Lethal Basilisk

In ancient and medieval times, stories of a lethal serpent known as the basilisk abounded. According to the Roman writer Pliny the Elder, the basilisk was a deadly foot-long snake that had a white, crown-like marking on its head. When it moved it did not coil its body from side to side but advanced straight, with its head raised from the ground. Its breath could destroy grass and smash rocks. Over time, other legends surrounded the beast. In later accounts it became a large cockerel with a serpent's tail (in which form it was also known as a cockatrice). It was said that its stare alone could kill everything it gazed upon!

DARK DESTROYERS

THE MONSTROUS GORGONS ARE AMONG THE MOST TERRIFYING BEINGS IN MYTH. THESE THREE SISTERS HAD HAIR CONSISTING OF WRITHING SERPENTS, AND THEIR STARES ALONE COULD TURN PEOPLE INTO STONE.

Just as sinister are the Furies and Harpies. Winged females, the Furies haunt wrongdoers while the hideous Harpies have women's faces combined with the body of a bird, and terrible long claws. They swoop down and snatch food away from tables, fouling everything they touch.

"They rip the feast to bits, making everything that they touch filthy. The sounds they make are ghastly, and the smell they give off nauseous."

– Roman poet Virgil describing the Harpies

Harpies

The name "Harpies" comes from the Greek word for "snatching", and this is what these flying monsters are notorious for. Perhaps the best-known episode involving the Harpies was their encounter with the Trojan hero Aeneas, during his voyage from Troy to Italy.

Avengers

Beware the dreaded Furies, for these spirits hunt down wrongdoers and deliver terrible punishments! The Furies are hideous winged women dressed in black robes; blood drips from their eyes and snakes twist in their hair. Victims of crimes can seek revenge by calling upon the Furies to pursue those responsible. They will show no mercy, often driving a guilty person to madness, or even death.

SNATCHERS FROM THE SKY

Aeneas and his men landed on the islands of the Strophades. As they sat down to eat, they heard the sound of beating wings and the Harpies were upon them. Swooping down and screeching, the creatures snatched the food and dirtied everything with their filthy claws.

The Trojans chose another more sheltered place to eat, but again the Harpies descended from the sky, carrying away the men's food. When the Harpies approached for the third time, Aeneas commanded his men to fight them. The Trojans slashed at them with their swords, eventually managing to beat the creatures back.

The Snake-headed Medusa

King Polydectes of Seriphos wanted to marry a beautiful woman named Danaë. But he was put off from doing so by her fine young son, Perseus, whose father was none other than Zeus, king of the gods. So one day, Polydectes asked Perseus to perform a quest: to bring back the head of Medusa, the most famous of the snake-headed gorgons. Polydectes was confident that Perseus would never return. For Medusa, like her two sisters, could turn everything she looked at into stone!

CUTTING OFF MEDUSA'S HEAD

After Perseus agreed to take on the challenge, the goddess Athena advised him to obtain some special equipment from the nymphs of the north. This consisted of winged sandals, a helmet that would make him invisible and a knapsack in which to place the gorgon's severed head. Perseus eventually found the nymphs, who were only too glad to give him these items. In addition, the god Hermes gave the hero a sword.

Properly equipped, Perseus flew off to the gorgons' cave. As he approached it, he saw the horrifying forms of people who had been turned to stone. Nevertheless, wearing his helmet, which made him invisible, and using his shield as a mirror – to avoid looking at the gorgons directly – he advanced into the cave. There he found the three monsters fast asleep. He edged nearer to them, raised his sword, and with a mighty swish chopped off Medusa's head. He then shoved it in his bag and flew off before the other two gorgons could catch him.

MONSTERS OF THE DEEP

SINCE ANCIENT TIMES, MARINERS' TALES HAVE TOLD OF HUGE AND VIOLENT
SEA MONSTERS ABLE TO DESTROY SHIPS WITH TERRIFYING EASE.

The Bible mentions Leviathan, who made the sea boil with the heat of its body, while in Greek myth, Scylla and Charybdis prey on sailors who try to find a safe passageway between them. In northern legends, the mighty Kraken, the size of an island, terrorizes ships sailing the seas off Scandinavia.

"Scylla tugged my wriggling companions up to the cliff, and there at the entrance of her cave she started eating them as they screamed."

– Odysseus describing Scylla in the Odyssey

Scylla and Charybdis

These terrible monsters live opposite each other in a strait formed by two great cliffs that jut up from the sea and lie an arrow's flight apart. On one of these rocks Scylla lives in a deep cave. Although she yelps like a small dog, she is in fact a fearsome monster, with 12 long feet dangling from the cave, and six necks each topped by a frightful head. Her mouths have three rows of closely packed teeth. From the depths of the cave she shoots out her heads and plucks away any creature unlucky enough to stray too near.

Sailors are advised to steer clear of Scylla's cave. But if they sail too close to the other rock, they risk being destroyed by Charybdis! This creature lies hidden beneath the water. Three times a day she sucks down the water above her, creating a huge dangerous whirlpool that can smash ships into bits of wood. She then spits out the water, sending it streaming through the air.

Odysseus Confronts the Monsters

The Greek hero Odysseus was forced to face these dreadful beasts on his return from Troy. He had to make a decision: should he risk Scylla or Charybdis? The Greeks rowed into the strait between the cliffs and soon saw the sea being sucked down by Charybdis. While the sailors were transfixed with fear, Scylla suddenly lunged out and snatched six of them from the ship. The men writhed in her grip as she swung them through the air and set them down at the entrance of her cave. Then, before the horrified eyes of their shipmates, Scylla began to devour them.

Odysseus's troubles were far from over. Some time later, the god Zeus destroyed the ship with a thunderbolt and the sailors plunged into the water to their doom. Odysseus managed to hang on to the wreckage and tie some of it together to form a raft, but then a south wind picked up and began to blow him back towards the rocky straits of Scylla and Charybdis! This time he came closer to Charybdis and sure enough the monster suddenly sucked down the sea, creating a vast gulf.

Odysseus Escapes

Odysseus would have sunk down along with his raft but for the fact he managed to cling onto the branch of a fig tree that stood on the rock. There he hung in terror, praying that the sea beast would spew out his raft. Finally, Charybdis shot out a spray of water and the hero's raft bobbed up to the surface. Immediately Odysseus dropped down onto the vessel and rowed rapidly away, finally managing to escape the two monsters.

WATER MAIDENS

THE OCEANS OF THE WORLD ARE SO VAST THAT IT IS NOT SURPRISING
SAILORS THROUGH THE AGES HAVE RETURNED HOME WITH TALES OF
STRANGE MARINE CREATURES.

One of these is the mermaid, whose pretty appearance is said to lure sailors to their deaths. Similar to mermaids are the Greek Sirens and the German Lorelei, water maidens whose sweet melodic singing draw mariners and their ships fatally onto the rocks.

Women of the Sea

Mermaids have the body of a beautiful young woman from the head down to the waist, and the tail of a fish below. Some dwell on rocks – where they can sit and comb their long hair – and others make their homes far below in the murky depths of the sea. There, it is said, they can imprison the souls of dead humans. Some mermaids have prophetic powers, able to predict the future. More often than not, they are seen as agents of death. The Morgans of Brittany in France, for example, can rise to the surface of the sea to embrace fishermen, sometimes killing them, and sometimes taking them down and forcing them to live in their watery homes.

Mermaid stories go back thousands of years. In the ancient Middle East, for example, the Syrian goddess Atargatis (known to the Greeks as Derceto) was said to have transformed into a mermaid. The story goes that she fell in love with a young shepherd and became the mother of their child. Ashamed at what had taken place, she threw herself into a lake in order to take the form of a fish. However, although her body took the shape of a fish, her head remained human.

The Rhine Maiden

In German folklore, a beautiful young woman named the Lorelei threw herself into the river Rhine after an unhappy love affair. After her death she could be seen sitting on a rock in the river, singing to passing ships. Sailors are transfixed by her beautiful music and row towards it, only to founder on the rocks and meet their doom...

The Bewitching Sirens

Living on an island surrounded by rocks, the Sirens were sea nymphs who sang so beautifully that passing sailors were enchanted by their songs and steered their ships towards them. The vessels would then be wrecked on the rocks, and the Sirens would kill them. The Greek heroes Jason and Odysseus both encountered these deadly nymphs.

Jason and his men, the Argonauts, sailed close to the Sirens' island during their quest to bring back the Golden Fleece from Colchis. As they heard the nymphs' beautiful voices wafting over the sea, one of their crew, the musician Orpheus, quickly took out his lyre and began to drown out their song with his playing. They were nearly past the danger when one of the Argonauts heard the music and plunged into the sea, swimming towards the island. But before he reached the Sirens, the goddess Aprhodite snatched him up, saving him from certain death.

TIED TO THE MAST!

Odysseus heard the Sirens on his way back from Troy. Warned about their music, he made sure that his sailors had their ears stuffed with wax. He himself was curious to hear the Sirens' songs, so he asked his men to tie him to the mast, and ordered them not to untie him, even if he begged to be freed!

When the Sirens saw Odysseus's ship coming, they began to sing. Deaf to the music, the crewmen continued to row, while Odysseus was smitten with the beauty of their voices. He indicated to his men that he wanted to be untied. But his companions wisely ignored him, and kept on rowing until they were well clear of the Sirens' menace.

MAGICAL HORSES

GODS AND HEROES OF LEGEND HAVE ALWAYS RELIED ON THEIR HORSES. WONDERFUL STORIES CONCERNING THESE GRACEFUL ANIMALS CAN BE FOUND IN MYTHS ACROSS THE WORLD.

The Greek hero Bellerophon was indebted to his winged steed Pegasus to help him kill the Chimera, while the Norse god Odin rode upon an eight-legged horse called Sleipnir. Perhaps the most magical of these horses, however, is the unicorn.

Unicorns

The western unicorn resembles a large, elegant white horse with a long, tapering horn. Some say it has the tail of a lion and the legs of a deer. The unicorn is mentioned by ancient Greek writers such as Herodotus and Ctesias, and Biblical legends say the creature was so big that it could not fit into Noah's ark and had to be towed behind the vessel! The unicorn horn is much valued for its power to detect poison in foods and cure various illnesses. Some say the sixteenth-century pope Paul III paid 12,000 gold pieces for a horn to ward off the plague!

How to Capture a Unicorn

According to an early Christian book called the *Physiologus*, the unicorn is small in stature and so fierce that it can be captured only by trickery. Here's how:

- If a unicorn is thought to dwell in a forest, a young maiden should be led among the trees.
- There she should wait alone for the unicorn to emerge from its lair. When the creature sees the girl, it will come over to her and place its head in her lap.
- The maiden should then stroke the unicorn's neck until it falls asleep, ready to be captured by waiting hunters.

UNICORNS OF THE EAST

Eastern unicorns are said to bring peace and good luck. In China, stories tell of the *qilin*, a unicorn-like creature that has a lion's head with a single horn, a scaly body and horses' hooves. They are said to be so gentle that they will take care not to tread on insects! Legend has it that the mythical Chinese emperor Fu Xi saw a *qilin* emerging from a river one day. On its back were strange symbols: the emperor copied these down and they became the basis for China's first written language.

"They have a horn on the forehead which is about a foot and a half in length."
– Greek writer Ctesias describing a unicorn

REAL OR FAKE?

The Unicorn Horn

The horn of the unicorn has been much prized through the centuries. Horns considered to be genuine were ground up and used to cure or prevent illnesses. The rich would pay high prices to buy such a horn. Not surprisingly, people were sometimes tricked into buying "false" unicorn horns – horns from animals such as goats or bulls.

Odin's Eight-Legged Horse

In Norse myths, Sleipnir is the mighty steed belonging to Odin, god of wisdom and war, and leader of the other gods. Sleipnir resembles a large horse, but with one crucial difference: he has eight legs instead of four! This gives him the speed and the power to carry his master from the world of the gods to earth.

Sleipnir's parents are the god Loki and a stallion belonging to a rock giant. The story goes that the giant had disguised himself as a stonemason and offered to build a wall around the gods' home of Asgard. In return he asked for the hand in marriage of the goddess Freyja, along with the sun and the moon.

THE GIANT REVEALED

Loki persuaded the gods to accept the giant's offer – on condition that the giant finished the wall within a certain period of time. The giant worked away, and soon the horrified gods realized that he would finish the wall in time if nothing was done to stop his progress. So Loki turned himself into a beautiful mare and lured the giant's stallion away. The giant was so furious that he let his disguise slip, revealing his true nature. Seeing who the stonemason really was, Thor, the god of thunder, smashed him on the head with his hammer! Later on, Loki gave birth to a horse – Sleipnir.

HELLISH HOUNDS

MONSTROUS SNARLING DOGS, SOMETIMES WITH MORE THAN ONE HEAD, OFTEN FEATURE AS GUARDIANS OF THE UNDERWORLD, THE REALM OF THE DEAD.

Perhaps the best known of these hellish hounds is Cerberus, the horrific three-headed beast that stands at the entrance of Hades, the Greek underworld.

The Hound of Hades

The Greek underworld, Hades, is a dark and terrifying place guarded by Cerberus, a monstrous three-headed dog. A ferocious beast with huge jaws full of deadly fangs, he allows the dead to enter Hades but prevents anyone from leaving. However, a few individuals have managed to pass in and out of Hades without being savaged by Cerberus. Orpheus was one. Famed for his music, he went in search of his beautiful young wife Eurydice, who had died of a snake bite. As he approached Hades, he began to play his lyre, and Cerberus was lulled to sleep, allowing the musician to slip past him.

CONFRONTING THE HOUND

Another to enter Hades was the Trojan Aeneas during his journey from Troy to Italy. Aeneas was accompanied by a prophetess known as the Sibyl, and both were confronted by Cerberus as they approached his cave. Sibyl threw the dog a honey cake that had been soaked in a sleeping potion. Cerberus gobbled up the cake and soon the dog's great body relaxed and sank to the ground. Aeneas and the Sibyl then walked past him into the depths of Hades.

Perhaps the best-known hero to confront Cerberus was Heracles. For the last of his famous 12 tasks or labours, he was asked to bring Cerberus up from Hades alive. Heracles descended into the underworld and the king of Hades agreed to let Heracles take the hound, as long as he did not damage him. Heracles then wrestled with Cerberus using his great strength to overcome him. The hero tied him to a strong chain and led him up to daylight.

"The noise of his dreadful barking, rising from his three throats, fills even the blessed dead with fear."

– Roman writer Seneca describing Cerberus

The Dogs of Yama and Garm

The sacred Hindu book *Rig Veda* mentions two dogs who perform a similar task to Cerberus. These are the dogs of Yama, lord of the spirits of the deceased. One of them is black, the other spotted, and both have four eyes. The dead have to pass by them on their way to join their ancestors, who are said to be rejoicing with Lord Yama.

In Norse mythology, the ferocious hound Garm also has four eyes. Huge in size, Garm lives in a cave and guards Helheim, the place of the dead. It was said that Garm's howling will signal Ragnarök – the end of the world.

Fenrir, the Giant Wolf

In Norse myth Fenrir is a monstrous wolf, the son of the god Loki and the giantess Angerboda. It is prophesied he will devour the god Odin when the world ends.

Fearing Fenrir, the gods decided to find a way to restrain him forever. Thinking they could trick him, the gods questioned Fenrir's strength and the wolf agreed to be bound in iron chains as a test. He easily broke free. Next, the gods asked dwarves to make them a magical chain. When it was finished it looked very fragile, but it was extraordinarily strong, the result of a strange mix of ingredients. When the gods challenged Fenrir with this ribbon, the wolf suspected a trick. He agreed to be bound up, but asked that one of the gods place his hand in his, Fenrir's mouth, as a token of good faith. Tyr, the war god, agreed, and the gods tied up the wolf. Try as he might, he could not break his bonds. In a moment of fury, Fenrir bit off Tyr's hand!

Fenrir's Unbreakable Bonds

Six weird and wonderful ingredients went into making Fenrir's magic chain:

- A cat's footsteps
- A mountain's roots
- A woman's beard
- A bear's sinews
- A bird's spittle
- Fishes' breath

WINGED WONDERS

FANTASTIC FLYING CREATURES HAVE FASCINATED PEOPLE FOR CENTURIES. PERHAPS THE MOST DRAMATIC OF THESE IS THE PHOENIX, RENOWNED FOR DYING IN A FIRE AND BEING REBORN.

In the West, stories about the phoenix are usually set in ancient Arabia and Egypt, and a similar type of bird can be found in the traditions of China and Japan. Two other types of winged creature that inspire awe in the West are the griffin, traditional guardian of hidden treasure, and its legendary offspring the hippogriff.

The Arabian Phoenix

Only one phoenix exists at any one time. This unique bird lives a long life – some say 500 years, though others believe it to be over one thousand! The bird is about the size of an eagle, but unlike the eagle it has brilliant, colourful plumage. Some who have been lucky enough to catch sight of this majestic creature say its shimmering feathers are deep red and golden, while others claim it has a tuft of feathers on its head, and that its body is glowing purple with an azure tail. Its song is melodic and mesmerizing.

The phoenix lives in the deserts of Arabia near a well. It soars up at dawn and sings a song that even the Greek sun god Apollo found bewitching. It is said to eat morning dew, though some claim all the phoenix needs in the way of food is the air itself or the sweet perfume of flowers.

Rising From the Ashes

The most extraordinary thing about the phoenix happens at the time of its death. When it knows it is dying, it starts to gather aromatic twigs and spices, and builds a nest out of them. Then it sits on the nest and sets it on fire, disintegrating in the flames. But this is not the end of the story, for as the fire consumes the bird, it is magically reborn from the blaze!

Some believe this happens straightaway; others that it occurs after the fire has died down. From the ashes a worm crawls out, turning into a new phoenix and taking off into the sky to start a new life.

In one tradition, the newborn bird gathers up the ashes of its predecessor and puts them in a ball of myrrh (a type of spice), which it has hollowed out. It seals the ball with fresh myrrh and carries it westward to Egypt. There, at Heliopolis – a city dedicated to the sun – the phoenix leaves the ashes on the altar of the temple.

> *"It is sacred to the sun, and is different to other birds in the colours of its feathers and the nature of its beak... The general tradition says [it lives] five hundred years."*
>
> – Roman writer Tacitus describing the phoenix

Griffins and Hippogriffs

Griffins are flying creatures with lions' bodies and the wings, heads and necks of eagles, along with horses' ears. They are believed to reside in the mountains of ancient Scythia, north of the Black Sea. There they live in golden nests and guard hidden treasure.

Griffins can have offspring known as hippogriffs ("hippo" comes from the Greek word for "horse"). These creatures resemble a griffin at the front and a horse at the rear. They are often ridden by sorcerers who prize them for their speed and power! In one story, the magician Atlantes, who lived on the border of France and Spain, owned a hippogriff. Atlantes kept his foster-son Rogero captive in his castle, and the beautiful warrior-maiden Bradamante tried to free him. Atlantes mounted his hippogriff and set out to kill the girl, but she managed to overpower him! Bradamante then rescued Rogero, who mounted the hippogriff and flew off at great speed.

SHAPE-SHIFTERS

SHAPE-SHIFTING IS A MAGICAL TRANSFORMATION FROM ONE FORM TO ANOTHER.
A SHAPE-SHIFTER CAN CHANGE FROM HUMAN TO ANIMAL, AND BACK AGAIN AT WILL.

Famous beings possessing this power include the Greek sea-god Proteus, who could turn into several animals in quick succession. Perhaps the most terrifying and dramatic shape-shifter of all is the werewolf, someone who can take the form of a wolf. The change from man to wolf traditionally takes place at full moon.

A Terrifying Beast

According to Ovid, there was once a king of Arcadia in Greece called Lycaon, notorious for his cruelty. One day, the god Zeus decided to visit the king and entered Lycaon's palace. The servants showed him great respect – much to the anger of Lycaon, who decided to kill Zeus. Before doing this, the king served the god a supper of human flesh and guts. Zeus was outraged and destroyed the palace with a thunderbolt.

Lycaon fled in terror and ran into the fields. There he howled aloud and began to attack the sheep. Then he found his clothes turning into bristles and his arms becoming furry legs. Now he could bound along on all fours – he had become a wolf! Only his eyes, still glittering with cruelty, remained from his old human form. This was Zeus's punishment of Lycaon for his wickedness.

How to Spot a Werewolf!

Werewolves are not easy to spot – look out for the following telltale signs among your friends and acquaintances!

- A fear of water
- Thick eyebrows that join at the middle
- Hair on the forehead that grows into a triangular "widow's peak"
- Bad sleepers who become increasingly restless towards the full moon
- Hands with hairy palms
- Deep, penetrating and often yellow eyes
- Unusual amounts of body hair
- A taste for eating raw meat.

"His clothing turned into bristling hair, his arms into legs. He had become a wolf! But a tiny part of his old human shape remained."

– Roman poet Ovid describing King Lycaon

From Soldier to Werewolf

The Roman writer Petronius wrote about a werewolf in ancient Italy. A slave named Niceros was walking with a soldier-friend in the country when they came to some tombs. There they rested. Then, before the astonished eyes of Niceros, the soldier stripped off his clothes, turned into wolf, howled and bolted for the woods! Terrified, Niceros hurried to a nearby farm. There he was told that a wolf had just attacked the sheep. One of the farmhands, however, had punctured the wolf's neck with a spear.

Niceros returned to the house of his friend. He found him lying in bed, with a doctor bandaging his neck. Niceros then realized the soldier must be a werewolf!

The Selkies

In Irish and Scottish folklore, selkies are seals who can change themselves into humans. They emerge from the sea as seals, then shed their skins and turn into ordinary people. But they need to keep their skins safe so that they can put them on and turn back into seals.

One tale tells of a fisherman who saw several selkies on the beach. They had just left their seal skins on a rock, so the man sneaked up and took one. When the selkies decided to return to the sea, one of them found her skin was missing: she was stranded on land! The fisherman took her home and made her his wife. Although she bore him children, the selkie pined for the sea. One day she discovered her old seal skin hidden away. At night, she fled the house and, putting on her skin, returned to the waves.

Proteus the Changer

Stories of shape-shifting were well known to the Greeks. Zeus, for example, changed into various forms, such as a bull, swan or shower of gold, to gain access to the women he had fallen in love with. Perhaps the best known Greek shape-shifter was Proteus, an old sea god who had the gift of prophecy, and who was known to change himself into anything from a panther or lion to a tree or running water. When someone asked him a question, Proteus avoided answering by changing his form!

THE END

THIS IS A CARLTON BOOK

Text and design copyright © Carlton Books Limited 2009
Illustrations copyright © Stuart Martin 2009

This edition published in 2009 by Carlton Books Limited
An imprint of the Carlton Publishing Group
20 Mortimer Street
London W1T 3JW

First published in 2008 by Carlton Books Limited

A catalogue record is available for this book from the
British Library.

10 9 8 7 6 5 4 3 2 1

ISBN: 978 1 84732 429 0

Printed and bound in China

Art director: Russell Porter
Senior executive editor: Stella Caldwell
Design: Andy Jones and Drew McGovern
Production: Lisa Moore